Bubbles!
¡Burbujas!

by Deborah Schecter

ISBN: 978-1-338-70284-2
Illustrated by Anne Kennedy
Copyright © 2020 by Deborah Schecter. All rights reserved.
Published by Scholastic Inc., 557 Broadway, New York, NY 10012

10 9 8 7 6   68   23 24 25 26/0

Printed in Jiaxing, China. First printing, June 2020.

■ SCHOLASTIC

Bubbles at the beach.

Burbujas en la playa.

Bubbles in the bath.

Burbujas en la bañera.

Bubbles in the sink.

Burbujas en el fregadero.

Bubbles in my drink.

Burbujas en mi bebida.

Bubbles in the clothes.

Burbujas en la ropa.

Bubbles that I blow.

Burbujas que yo hago.

Bubbles, bubbles, bubbles,
everywhere I go!

¡Burbujas, burbujas,
por donde quiera que voy!